Life Begins Now!
How exciting is that?..!
- Marilyn

Live life your way - Don't Land.

Sali

4/18

i

28 Day Sculpting Challenge

Utilizing Energy Magnetism to Sculpt the Life You Want to Live

Marilyn Lawrence and Dale Lawrence

Copyright © 2016 by Marilyn Lawrence

Library of Congress Cataloging-in-Publication Data

Lawrence, Marilyn
28 Day Sculpting Challenge/28 Day Sculpt Your Life Challenge / Marilyn Lawrence.
p. cm.

ISBN: 978-0-9915707-2-0

1. Energy Magnetism 2. Soul-Essence 3. Goal Attraction

Printed in the United States of America
Dragonfly Media, LLC

*"We are living in the **Gestation of Our Actions.***

Don't like what you have grown?

Plant New Seeds!*"*

Table of Contents

Day 1- Sunday

The Beginning of Your Shift

"For every action there is a reaction.
Awareness of action prevents derailment and distraction."

We want to first thank you for joining us, and for taking the time and making the effort to formulate advancements in your life. Because of you, the world is a more beautiful place.

Today, the first day of your 28 Day Sculpting Your Life Challenge is your "Prep" day.

"The Key to success is in the hands of the driver.
Turn it on and hit the gas." Dale Lawrence

The 28 Day "Sculpting Your Life" Challenge

Every Morning upon rising and every evening when retiring I send gratitude and appreciation.

I Thank God, (you may speak with whomever you choose) and his Angels, my Guides, Council and Guardian Angels for giving me another day, for all the information and healing they bring to me and for all the good they do for me, my family and loved ones, the world and the universe, every day in every way.

This is a wonderful practice. Stating that you do realize that you receive help, showing appreciation for it, and thus, by this acknowledging, attracting more.

When you are sending appreciation be specifically positive. If a thought like, "but I had a bad day" sneaks in, remember, you do not want to magnetize that energy by giving it attention. It may be fact, but dwelling on that energy will bring more of the same. You are intentionally promoting the energy that you want to radiate around you. The energy you need to sculpt the life you want.

So if your thoughts go to "But I had a bad Day." Look for something, even if it is just one thing in the day that you can show appreciation for. Give that good your attention and fight off the urge to give attention to the negative. That does not justice.

"Do not let fear hold you back from doing the things that you want or should be doing. You agreed to a purpose when you came to this life. If it were unobtainable, you never would have agreed to do it." Marilyn Lawrence

Assignments:
Your day of preparations.

What you will need:

> **Post-it Notes- Just how serious are you about the life that you desire? Rather Deserve? (!)**

Included with this workbook you received post-it notes. You may need to purchase more. Your commitment will directly affect your outcome. These post-it notes will be used to reinforce your commitment to the shifts needed to sculpt the life you desire.

Plan on Putting Them Everywhere! Examples: "I Am Attracting Abundance of all that is Good." "I Am Successful." I Am Living Life Aligned with My Greatest Good." "I Am Abundantly Happy." I Am…..

Your thinking: This or something more.

Do Not skimp! Do Not limit yourself.

Your daily assignments will direct you what to write and how.

> ➤ Goal/Vision Board. If you have not already, you will need to purchase a large piece of poster board. Choose a size that matters.

This will be used as your goal/visual board to commit, and then remind you just how beautiful your reality and goals are. Taking the time to perform the physical act of applying them to a board, and then placing the goal board in a location that will be seen daily, amplifies the effectiveness. If you do not have some, pick up some markers and any other tools that you want to use to create the projection of your life, like a glue stick, sharpies, three-D items, magazines. Anything that will make your vision board more realistic and empowering to you. Use markers in colors that represent importance to you. Green- Go? Healing? Growth? Red-important? Blue- Calm? Balanced? Healing? Orange- Happy? Yellow- Mental Clarity? Whatever colors you are automatically drawn to are the colors that you need now, and whatever you feel/think the colors mean to your advancement. I have just given examples above.

Don't forget glitter, because your future is looking very bright and shiny.

> ➤ **Mindset:**

Abundance IS YOUR Reality. Having bad relationships, attracting the wrong people, living with less than you need, not being in joy, and etc., is NOT your

Reality! Be prepared to embrace the change required to shift old patterns and effectively move into desired patterns and outcomes.

Embracing a philosophy of faith and trust, without doubt and over-thinking/analyzing is imperative. Commit to performing each assignment without reluctance and second-thinking.

Change is difficult sometimes. Reluctance to take an avenue that is not familiar creates apprehension and fear of the unknown for some.

Change takes change.

After all, how many 28 day segments have passed where you have worked in the reality of your old thinking and actions, just to have the same life the next day?

Commit to your dreams, your goals, and your life's mission statement!

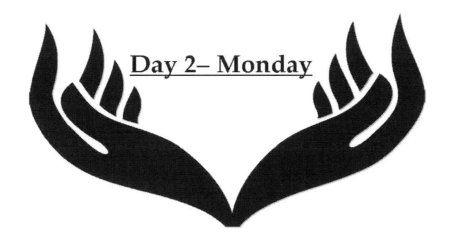

Day 2– Monday

"The future is yours. It belongs to you. It is your undiscovered life. Embrace it, take control of it and inspire yourself." Dale Lawrence

Good Monday Morning!

Beginning the awareness.
Two simple assignments today based on- **Be and then Do.**

I looked up the definition of Mon, (Mon day) and here is what I found:
Definition of mon-
    1.   *: one : single : alone <monosyllable>*

Interesting, isn't it? This is a similar feeling that I hear from many people I work with. The feeling of being alone or lonely....

For those that experience this feeling periodically, I hope that you will write your post-it notes to change the vibration in you. "I Am one with all and thus, loved by all." I Am Loved," "I Am always connected," "I have many friends," and etc.

Fight back the urge to question and condemn the counter-action words you write.... for you would be condemning the fact that you deserve to live in them.

As I mentioned, it may be a struggle at first to write things that are not PERCEIVED as your reality. Perceived is the key word. You have the right to perceive things anyway you want them.

Sculpt your life!

"Every word, thought, action, and emotion carries energy. Whatever you say to yourself or to others carries energy. That energy creates a charge that is sent out around you." Marilyn Lawrence

Assignments:

> **BE-** Today, Monday, will be the first day back to work for many of you since embarking on the sculpting project. What this means is wonderful really; it gives you more opportunities to see, (Be) the things that create residual triggers that do not line up with your intentions and visions of you.

> ## DO-

1). Keep this workbook handy and write below everything that happens- words, actions, and thoughts, that don't <u>feel good</u>…that are the reverse of what you want in your life. Next to each, at the same time, (or later after having considered), write next to each what you would rather think, feel or do. The action that will counter-balance the vibration that is not welcome to you. Does that make sense?

An example: "Ruth is so condescending and fickle, she never does her fair share around her and I am left doing most of the work." Post-it note- "I AM fully supported and have all the help I need." "I AM capable of doing all this work and more without it affecting me poorly." Whatever rings truth to you. But do this. Put yourself in the position of where you want to be. Do not feed that which bothers you, feed that which you want. Don't mull on Ruth's perceived ineffectiveness, mull o how lucky you are to have all the help in the world you need at any time you need it.

Another example: "He is so mean and cranky to me. I just don't like being around him." Post-it: I AM so lucky to have someone love me enough to share lessons with me. I AM better because of the lessons." "I AM attracting all the love and support I need in life."

So today, **Be** in your space, and **Do** the things necessary to align with your truths and goals.

We are here to help you if you need us.
Sending you all pure love!!!

"Create 'milestones' for your path to success. Break the big picture into smaller achievable pieces and then focus on the destination while concentrating on the process and let go of the results, they are byproducts of your belief system." Dale Lawrence

Day 3– Tuesday

Good Tuesday Morning!

"YOU ARE THE GREATNESS OF YOUR DESIRES!" Marilyn Lawrence

You have three, (3) assignments today.

Oops....what did your thinking do when you read this? A positive yahoo reaction knowing that you are taking hands on approach to your reality, or the reverse? Perhaps a reaction like, "I simply don't have time for this today?" If it was the latter, then you are telling the universe you do not have time to have the life you want, so you will just stay where you are.

How does that feel?

Not good?

Disappointing?

Or are you still mad and mulling over the perceived thought that you don't have time?

It is your life. Move your dial. Take 7 breathes and ground yourself. Then bring in the true light of you.

I promise you, this will work. Don't let yourself down.

I believe in you!

 I looked up the definition for Tue, (Tue sday)

Verb[edit]
tue to do

Interestingly, I looked up Tues, (Tues day) and this is the definition:

Noun[edit]
TUEs

1. *plural of* *TUE*

"Give your dreams life. Feed them as you feed yourself. Nurture them as you nurture your children. Love them as you love life, for they are your life. Believe in them and they will grow strong, mature, and inspire you." Dale Lawrence

Assignments:

> **1).** Your **first assignment** is "TO DO" ... and do it more.

Consciously participate in recognizing your "energy triggers" that have drawn to you what you do not like in your life. Identify and then create the cure.

Write below all the words, actions and thoughts that you recognize as creating energy attractions that you no longer desire. Examples: "I am not very good at this," "I don't have enough money to…"

_____

_____

_____

_____

_____

_____

_____

_____

➤ **2).** Your **second assignment** is to Keep yourself grounded and to check your grounding cord often.

A grounding cord is an invisible connection from you to something else, generally the center of the earth, though there are variations. If you successfully use grounding cord now, then continue. If you do not, or wish to vary your practice, try different methods until you find one that resonant with you. Staying grounded helps with multiple things including feeling less, "flighty," the ability to come up with answers quicker, evening out moods, and operating in balance. For a good solid grounding, run your grounding cord from your root chakra energy center, located at the base of your tailbone area, all the way to the Divine Crystalline Center. In my book, "On An Angel's Wing" the Angels shared that the Divine Crystals are available for our use again. They had been hidden for centuries.

My grounding cord is a tree trunk. I have asked the Angels to multiple the cords and increase their length to amp up the grounding abilities. The trees roots wind down through the earth and hold on securely to the Divine Crystalline center. Powerful!

The more you work on grounding, the more you will be able to tell the difference and reap the benefits.

Record your experiences with grounding below:

_____

_____

_____

_____

_____

_____
_____
_____
_____
_____
_____
_____
_____
_____
_____
_____
_____
_____
_____
_____
_____
_____
_____
_____
_____
_____
_____
_____
_____

> 3). Your **third assignment** is to **Chant** yourself to sleep tonight.

Chanting is an ancient, effective practice. We will be using chanting in its simplest of forms. The benefits are in-line with our energy magnetism. Instead of going to bed and filling your mind full of the problems of the day, or the anticipated problems of tomorrow, you will use disciplined statements repeated over and over until you fall to sleep.

Taking control of what you want your life to look like is your goal in these 28 days. Utilizing different methods will accelerate results.

Your sleeping hours are the longest period of time that you are at rest. Allowing the physical vessel to recharge, and allowing your mind and soul to rejuvenate and work on things. Control what it works on. Not chaos and drama, but instead positive advancements towards goals. Do not take the stresses of the day or the perceived problems of tomorrow with you to sleep. This just keeps the frustrations, anger, stress in your space, blocking conscious advancement and duties, plus, allowing them to fester in your physical body eventually causing dis-ease.

I have chanted the following for the last several years, adding when I go through different progressions or deadlines. "I Am Happy. I Am Healthy. I Am Wealthy. I Am Wise." Determine what you want to manifest at night. Always start with "I Am."

List some chants below and add to the list as you progress. Use your Claire sense to know which resonant with you're the most.

This is about you. Molding and sculpting you! IT is important.

The universe does not recognize time as we do. They will give you as much time as you need....even in continuing lives if you do not do what you want in this life.

Why not just do it now? In This Life? Why carry it forward? Leave your next life to creating even bigger and better possibilities?

Live

 Live the life you want to live now.

Everything is easy.

Do not make it hard!

"Together we can make a universal shift

to the pursuit of chosen design and destiny simply by

bringing consciousness to the forefront of thinking."

Marilyn Lawrence

Day 4– Wednesday

wed

(wĕd)

v. wed·ded, wed or wed·ded, wed·ding, weds

v.tr.

1. To take as a spouse; marry.

2. To perform the marriage ceremony for; join in matrimony.

3. To unite closely: *a style that weds form and function.*

4. To cause to adhere devotedly or stubbornly: *He was wedded to the idea of building a new school.*

v.intr.

Wednesday represents different things to different people, and is even identified with various names like, "hump day," "Wacky Wednesday" and more. I looked up the definition and its origin above. Take a look closely at #3 and #4, to unite closely; to cause to adhere devotedly or stubbornly.

A perfect philosophy to embrace today- Unite with the truths of you and devote yourself to creating the energy that you want to call back to you. Powerful day! Take advantage of its energy and effectiveness.

So, how are you doing with monitoring your thoughts, words and actions?

I know some of you may still be thinking that you don't have time for this; it may almost make you frustrated or angry to read through this because your life is perceived to be just too busy for anything else.

I read an article that relayed common thought patterns and attitudes of very successful people in different fields, from politicians to actors, musicians to financiers. The one thing that struck me is each monitored their intentions, consciously aware of the law of attraction. And, each never said they were <u>too busy</u>. That last statement has stayed with me. Of course it makes sense. When you tell the universe you are too busy, you are saying I can take no more, thus, you are given no more.

Are you too busy to accept your goals?

NO! Those are the things that you dream about, manifest and have now dedicated 28 days to sculpting.

So part of today's assignment is to monitor every time you think, say or feel that you are **too busy** to take on anything else. Tally the number of times you think this and write this number below, and date it. It will be quite interesting for you to see the number count on these old patterns as time progresses.

_____

_____

_____

_____

_____

_____

_____

_____

_____

_____

_____

_____

_____

_____

Yah but I am busy. Yup…we all are. It is a fact that time is moving faster. There is less time in the day and more things to do. That is why making conscious usage of time is essential. But, are you too busy for what you want? If someone gave you the golden ticket would you be too busy to accept it? The things that we ask do not take much time for the huge benefit. Trust me. Trust God and his Angels. Trust the universe.

Assignments:

So today, on this day of uniting and adhering closely with the vision of your life you are sculpting, your assignments are:

1). Write down every time your thoughts, words or actions regress to the "Too Busy" energy vibration.

2). Write an "I Am" next to each to reprogram the thinking. Something that registers and makes sense to you. "I Am busy, but never too busy for the life I Am sculpting."

3). Write down every time you catch yourself saying, doing or thinking counter-productive things. These may be regular offenders and you may begin to see a pattern. Next to each come up with an "I Am."

➤ **4).** Close your eyes, feet flat on the floor. Ground yourself. In your minds-eye, look at yourself in the bathroom mirror. How are you looking today? What makes you smile? Write it down. What makes you send disapproving thoughts to yourself. Write it down. How does this compare to your list at the workshop Saturday? Now shift the vibration of the thoughts, feelings and actions to bring what you want to look at. Create your "I Am's" for the next viewing.

➤ **5).** Send me your list of things that you are having a tough time counter-balancing, and we will ask the Angels for help for you.

<u>Remember to Ground yourself regularly.</u>

It is a beautiful day to unite with what makes you want to do the **Snoopy Dance**.

Step into that joyous reality. You have the God-given right to be happy, healthy, wealthy and _____ and _____ and_____.

"We create all of our memories.
They are the documentary of our lives and we write the scripts.
Live life so you can enjoy the re-runs, and
let go of the things you can not change." Dale Lawrence

Day 5– Thursday

Good Thursday morning!

I found enjoyment in researching the day of the week, such as today's- "Thurs." It is interesting to understand the thinking, and thus, energy behind each day's name. Taking it a step further, it is advantageous to utilize the energy behind a word to further intentions.

Today- "Thurs"day: Thurs

From Wikipedia, the free encyclopedia

Thurs, also Thurse, a mythological race with superhuman strength in Norse mythology.   Thurs, a math-statistical function.

So today, **let's call in both** the superhuman strength energy of the word, and also the calculating-statistical energy. Call on this energy throughout the day when you need it. Why not? The day was named for this energy, **why not utilize it?** What could it hurt?

How are you doing? No, really....how Are you doing? I have only heard back from a couple of you, so everyone else must be doing marvelously, without **set-back?** Right…..

I understand that to **change the programming** that you have supported for many years is difficult. You have programmed your thoughts actions and words with little to no awareness of the effects, and now you are stepping into the space of controlling them, being aware of them, and shifting them.

Alteration Takes Action.

"Regret is the outcome of unconscious actions."

Marilyn Lawrence

You don't take a pair of pants in to the tailor to have them alter the length and then they hand them back to you untouched. They take action to alter the item to satisfy your request.

Altering your energy intentions so that your ship may sail to the horizon of your choosing takes action…Active participation between you and the thing that requires altering.

I have worked with some people who only come to me when their life is in **unraveling chaos**. Of course we are able to smooth out the static, and of course, we give tools to aid them in handling the items that contribute to their mounting disarray. The unfortunate thing is they do not use them, or they are really good for a week or two and then slowly slip back in to **old habits**. It takes discipline and a conscious awareness of your space. …Your space that you created with your actions, words and thoughts.

I was talking with a dear friend, relaying how my husband and I had been **given some big lessons**. We had lost loved ones, we had been entered in to situations that before would have made us spiral out of control, allowing the **"lack-of"** to come in, fear of loss, fear of financial strain, doubt, and the like. But this time, with these lessons, we stood strong…utilizing superhuman strength…rather our own God-given strength to control our actions, and thus, **our reality**.

Through each situation, I explained, we **kept the faith** that all was happening for our highest and greatest good.

Many times I had to repeat that over and over until the spikes of anxiety relaxed.

And, guess what?

This disciplined action worked. Keeping the Faith, asking God and the Angels for help, monitoring thoughts, actions and words created opportunities for us that we only dreamt possible before.

We made our dreams, reality.

We were given lessons that lined up with our assignments for this life and we consciously participated.

That is why the Angels asked me to create the 28 Day Sculpting. They first had to provide for me several opportunities to learn the effectiveness, and then they asked me to teach others. **Powerful!**

I said all that to say this… I understand! IS it difficult to be consciously aware all the time? Yes! But, when you slip, recognizing it is the first step to change. Now, I am not suggesting that you stay in the "recognizing stage" indefinitely, but it is a start. When I learn things, the Angels tell me to appreciate the fact that I have taken a step forward. When you recognize that you have done something that is not in line with your horizon, commend yourself! It is a step forward.

Next step? Creating the "I Am's" to generate the alteration.

"We are the architects of all of our Dreams, all of our

Aspirations and all of our Life.

Build a palace."

Dale Lawrence

Assignments:

So on this day supported by superhuman power energy and calculating-statistical energy your **assignments are**:

> **1).** Write down every time you recognize that you have done, said, and felt something that is out of line with your horizon.

➤ **2).** Commend yourself for the steps forward. List below the number of times that you commend yourself, And, for what.

➤ **3).** Email me with thoughts, questions, or a thumbs-up.

➤ **4). Belly laugh at least once.**

We are Proud of you. We Believe in you! We are sending you Pure Love!

Day 6– Friday

Good Friday Morning!

To follow tradition of name definition, and utilize Friday's energy, here is the definition for Friday:

Friday is associated in many cultures with the love goddess Venus, and the planet named for her.

The name *Friday* comes from the Old English *Frīgedæġ*, meaning the "day of Frige", a result of an old convention associating the Old English goddess Frigg with the Roman goddess Venus, with whom the day is associated in many different cultures. Greek: to prepare." In Arabic : congregation/gathering.

So….Friday is about Love, Preparing and Gathering. What better day to give yourself the extra love and encouragement?

It has been a long week. Things have come up. You have kicked yourself, done and said things, caught yourself and have then felt guilty. You have second-thought participation. You have second-thought your life, and yourself. We have stirred the pot so you are aware of the "gunk" that floated to the bottom. Perfect time for plucking it out of your space!

So today let's call in the energy of Venus to surround us with love. Venus is VERY strong. Do not doubt the power of utilizing this beautiful energy. Do not limit the power.

 I will send the Angels to each of you to ask them to remind you of the feeling of Divine love.

"Do not let **fear or doubt** hold you back from doing the things that you want or should be doing.

We all have a **big picture to paint**, so do not spend too much time and energy in the same corner. " Marilyn Lawrence

Assignments:

> **1).** **Ground yourself**, (you should be doing this regularly by now, right?) Feet flat on the floor. Close your eyes. **With pure intention allow the energy of both Venus' love and the Angelic love to come to you**. Let this love permeate every bit of your mind, body and soul.

Feel the magnificence of radiating with love. Allow these love energies to wrap around your heart and heart chakra, flowing through it, cleansing it and replacing anything that is not love and your highest and greatest good.

Allow this love energy to dissolve any feelings of unloved you harnessed against yourself and others, against situations and perceived problems. Stay with this until you feel **the energy tingling through you.** Know that when you feel the "truth bumps," you are consciously creating a better space for yourself…you are filled with love for others, your life and **most importantly, YOU!**

Record the experience in detail below.

_____

_____

_____

_____

_____

_____

_____

_____

> **2). Review your list of frequent stumbles, at the end of your manual**…the things you have jotted down all week that you caught yourself, saying, doing or thinking. If you have not written anything down, **start.** Think back on your week and make notes. The time you had frustrating interactions with others, with your family and loved ones. The times you were _less than supporting_ to yourself. Write them down.

Remember, we are **modifying behavior** to create better. You cannot do that effectively if you do not **create an awareness** of what needs to be shifted.

> **3).** This evening before climbing into bed, look at yourself in your mirror **with eyes open.** Tell yourself (in your mind's eye, or aloud), how much you love yourself. Fight off the urge to condemn or judge.

Remember, "Judging is the cement that prevents progression."

Pull in Venus' Love and the Angelic Love, and ask that this **unparalleled love energy** permeate every bit of your mind, body and soul as you sleep.

> **4). Chant** your "I Am's" until you fall to sleep.

You are taking control of your life.

You are making your life what you want.

You have the power to do it with simple methods.

You are vibrating at your own tone.

You are bringing you home!

We are proud of you!

I am here to help if you need me!

"Opportunities in life are often elusive, like the quick scent of an unknown flower on the wind. It may require effort to discover.

But once discovered, they can be the most rewarding." Dale Lawrence

Day 7– Saturday

Happy Saturday and Day 7!

Satur : I satiate, sate, satisfy. **Saturday:** The Romans named Saturday *Sāturni diēs* ("Saturn's Day") no later than the 2nd century for the planet Saturn, which controlled the first hour of that day. Sabbath Day.

Tomorrow marks the first email I sent out with the 28 Day Sculpting information and assignments.

I write the emails based on the directions I receive. They are designed to keep you motivated, remind you of your Divine beauty, and lend support as you progress in your life sculpting.

You are not letting me down if you do not do the assignments, or make efforts. The Angels told me long ago, though they are saddened when they watch souls not operating in-line with their written missions/wishes, giving up on themselves and becoming a diluted version of themselves, the Angels know all things will happen in time. And, since Angels do not recognize time the same as we do in the human realm, their reference to time is based on their own. In the human realm we measure our soul's time based on the number of years we are here to contribute.

So, Angels know in their time-based reality all souls will make their designated progressions.

The cool thing is, we can control our advancements. By taking steps, even little steps, to better ourselves, we can control the speed. What does it mean to be progressing along your path? What is the outcome of doing so? It means being more consciously aware of the vibration you send out and how it is affecting the ones around you, the world and the universe, especially in comparison to what you wrote on your mission statement, and it creates happiness, satisfaction, and a sense of completeness when you do.

Are these daily assignments too long to read?

Do you not have time to read them, let alone do them?

What other reasons have you found not to focus on YOU? Because that is what it is, Giving to You.

Making time for You.

Dedicating you, to YOU.

Knowing that doing so will have a significantly positive effect on you, your family and loved ones, not to mention the universe.

Assignments:

> **1).** Yesterday, one of your assignments was to tell yourself you **love yourself**. Today, you are going to remind yourself that you are **dedicated to yourself**.

Stand in front of the mirror, **eyes open**, looking at you. Tell yourself a minimum of **7 times** each the following
dedications:

a). I Am Dedicated to making things better for ME.

b). I Am Dedicated to finding MYSELF again.

c). I Am dedicated to living in Joy.

d). I Am Dedicated to drawing all energies that align with MY highest and greatest good.

e). I Am Dedicated to shifting the energies that created hardships for ME.

f). I Am Dedicated to fulfilling MY mission statement for this life.

g). I Am Dedicated to ME.

> **2).** Review your **goal board.** What do you want to add? What do you want to change for the good? Modify it when you want. Make a new one when you have achieved the old desires. Write below how you have modified it today.

_____

_____

_____

_____

_____

_____

"Be very mindful and monitor your speech and actions

so the energy and charge you send out are

what you want to contribute to the world

and what you want to receive back." Marilyn Lawrence

> **3).** Email me **your biggest struggles**. We will call in **Angelic** help for you. We are in this together, and it is my position and pleasure to help you.

I Am Dedicated to you, as is God, His Angels, your Guides, Council and Guardian Angels. Since most of us work with multiple realms, you can call in all Divine-Mastery level or better assistance.

How could there possibly be a better time to start than now?

"Know that in every Sunrise there are a thousand possibilities, and that at every Sunset you can relive the ones you embraced."

Dale Lawrence

There are people that find reasons why they can't do something, placing blame on anything they can, spending time and energy on the problem.

And there are people that see a problem and spend time and energy on a solution, or ignore the problem all together, thus giving it no energy.

Check to make sure you are not spending time looking for problems or blaming things for your life's progression. You have the solution. Focus on that.

Day 8– Sunday

<u>Happy Sunday</u> and the beginning of week two on the path to the new vibration of you…**because of and thanks to you!**

"There are no accidents,

only experiences that we have the free will to make into

miracles—or not.

Many blessings with all your miracles!" Marilyn Lawrence

Since I missed sharing the definition of Sunday on last week's assignment, here is the definition for fun and energetic support.

Sunday: The day of rest and dedication. The first day of the week, observed as the Sabbath by most Christians sects.

WHEW! You did it! One week down, three more to go. By now, if you have been dedicating to <u>yourself</u> and the <u>assignments</u>, you should be feeling differently. A little more alive.

Though some transformations take time, others happen almost instantaneously. The interesting fact about this observation is the ones that have positive and dedicated applied intention behind them happens more seamlessly than those that have periodic doubt or fear-resistant triggers.

In conjunction, sometimes we do not see shifts immediately because things are brought to us when it is the right time to receive them based on the alignment to our life's schedule. The secret is to practice unequivocal faith, and monitor obstructive thinking.

You will feel lighter as you are releasing the heavy energy that is weighing you down and holding you back, replacing it with lighter energy that is reigniting your soul's light.

There should be **no day** that goes by from this day forward, that you do **not modify words, actions, and thinking** that do not <u>pull to you</u> the energy outlined in your goal vision of self. The more consciously you practice **energy magnetism**, the more you will notice when the "yucky" stuff comes in.

This alone is huge! To consciously recognize that which does you no good, and to reach for **phraseologies that counter-balance.** Breaking through the **cement caused by judgment** which has kept you stationary and has made it difficult to move forward, <u>is a feat too.</u>

Taking a broom to judgment like sweeping the dirt particles off a floor becomes easier and easier. The once perceived heavy mounds become just sprinklings of dust here and there, giving way to the invited energies of intention.

Remember the first time you rode your bike without training wheels? Or the first time you attempted throwing the ball to make a basket, or hit a tennis ball over the net? It took a few times, it took practice. <u>Few things are done perfectly or well the first time.</u>

So, too, does that principle apply to these achievements? But think about it…the simple practice of shifting words, thought patterns, and actions will <u>create limitless possibilities in the destination of your life.</u>

In comparison to other things you take time practicing, creating the life you want certainly **deems a worthy usage of time,** in my estimation.

How did yesterday's dedication exercise go? Repeating dedications to you is a good thing <u>to practice regularly</u>. In fact, one of today's assignments will utilize the same principle.

"You are only limited by who you believe you can be. Believe in yourself and your potential. Say it out loud every day.

Convince yourself, and you will convince the world," Dale Lawrence

Assignments:

1). Using the energy of the day, (**Sunday:** The day of rest and dedication).

- ➢ Dedicate and give thanks to God or the Source you speak with.

- ➢ Dedicate and give thanks to God's Angels and the ArchAngels, The Divine Mastery level, and whomever else you want to give appreciation too.

- ➢ Feel the *deep unconditional love from connection to Divine* as you show your upmost appreciation. The love warms your heart and continues throughout the rest of your body, mind and soul. This dedication and love you are sending is reciprocated filling you with even more.

- ➢ Write dedications below, (Minimum of five), and your feelings as you sent and received the dedications and love.

Maintain the same unconditional love "glow" as achieved in assignment #1 as you complete the rest of your assignments…better yet, the rest of your life!.

2).

- ➢ Look at yourself in the mirror.

- ➢ Send unconditional love to yourself.

- ➢ **Look deeply into your eyes**.

- ➢ Notice the **colors** in your eyes.

- ➢ Notice the **designs** in your eyes.

- ➢ **Smile** as you look at yourself.

- ➢ Notice your **wrinkles.**

- ➢ **Send love** to each one, knowing that each has been placed there based on experiences in your Divinely-stamped life.

- ➢ Send love to your **heart chakra**.

- ➢ Ask the Angels to show you **how to love yourself** as much as they love you.

- ➢ List your reactions when you look at yourself, (The good, bad and ugly reactions). Minimum of five.

> What was your reaction when you asked the Angels to show you how to love you as much as they love you? What triggers did you experience? Doubt, guilt? Hesitation?

List a minimum of five. Dig deep. Be Honest.

_____

_____

_____

_____

_____

_____

_____

_____

_____

_____

_____

3).

> Look back in the mirror at yourself.

> **Tell yourself, and list below a minimum of seven, (7) positive I Am's** based on the feelings and thoughts that were illuminated doing the above exercises.

_____

_____

_____

_____

_____

_____

_____

_____

_____

It may be that you have to correct some thoughts, and say I Am's to balance the less-than-positive triggers that were revealed. You have spent time in your life "beating yourself up" over different things that these exercises are designed to reveal and bring to the surface so you can release them and thus, their effects on you. Remember to **wrap each in the Angelic love** that God and his Angels have for you. Allow the warmth of pure love to permeate your heart chakra, and then **radiate out** through the rest of your being.

> ➤ **Tell yourself, and list below a minimum of seven, (7) not-so positive I Am's** based on the feelings and thoughts that were illuminated doing the above exercises.

> ➤ Next to each write a counter-balance- something that reduces their charge and shifts it to a positive towards your goal. Example: "I have no money." Correction: "I Am Wealthy." "I Am Abundance of all that is good." "I Am Abundantly Wealthy and etc...

> ➤ Make post-it notes for each positive above and POST THEM EVERY WHERE!

4). Add to your goal board any that you want included in your life.

If you are having trouble writing your I Am's, your post-it notes, or your goals, then please reach out to me. **Together we will call in Angelic help for you.**

I am dedicated to you, and I am here to help you. The Angels are here to help you, God, the Masters; the Universe is here to help you! When you are working and living in your purpose, you have universal support!

Simply call on us!

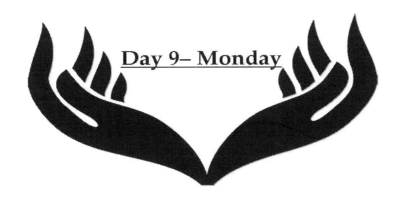

Day 9– Monday

Good Monday Morning!

And, what a beautiful day it is. Another day closer to radiating with the full truths of you, thanks to the dedications you are gifting yourself. Dedicating time to you, Attracting to you, consciously, what you want and how you want your life to be. Big Stuff!

I have included quotes that I receive via many sources. I have found it quite interesting how they parallel our sculpting work, and, how long the idea of positive affirmations, worded in different ways, has been suggested and used. If something did not work, it would never weather the test of time.

Positive affirmations, attracting what you want to you based on your words, thoughts and actions, does work. Modifying behavior to incorporate the practice is the challenge for some. Some still operate in the doubt or judgment mode. Doubt that it will work; I don't have time for it, and etc. All your choices.

You may believe what you want to believe until you believe something else. We will give you the information, we will leave a trail of breadcrumbs to a brighter tomorrow, and you can decide when you want to eat.

Last Monday, based on the definition for the day, your assignments were:

"BE- Today, Monday, will be the first day back to work for many of you since embarking on the sculpting project. What this means is wonderful really; it gives you more opportunities to see the things that create residual triggers that do not line up with your intentions and visions of you.

DO- Keep a pad of paper handy and write down everything that happens, words, actions, and thoughts that don't feel good. That are the reverse of what you want in your life. Next to each, at the same time, or later after having considered, write next to each what you would rather think, feel or do. The action that will counter-balance the vibration that is not welcome to you.
Does that make sense?"

We will concentrate on these again.

Considering it takes time to change a habit, according to, Dr. Maxwell Maltz 21 Days, though his research was modified to include, "Depending on the individual," it was proven in every case that intent played a large role in the outcome. Whether or not the individual participating in the <u>modification behavior used full intention</u>.

So beginning today, <u>lace every move</u> forward with **"Full, Pure Intentions."** Using pure intentions is eliminating any doubt, doing it fully is committing yourself completely to something.

"Pay Attention

by creating a consciousness to the effects of current

behavioral patterns,

and then suggest a shift in the awareness to a pursuit of

individual purpose." Marilyn Lawrence

Assignments:

1).

➤ With <u>Full Pure Intentions</u> **DO-** Keep this workbook or a pad of paper handy, and write down words, actions, and thoughts throughout the day that **don't feel good, that leave you in a bad mood, make you angry, sad, and hurt and etc., the energies** that are the reverse of what you want in your life. This could be because of your actions, or because of another's actions. Some of our biggest lessons are via observation and orchestration because of it. This is a hands-on reality check!

➤ Next to each, write what you would rather think, feel or do. The action that will counter-balance the vibration that <u>is not welcome to you, and you certainly do not want back!</u>

2).

➤ Was it your action that requires correcting, or was it another's that provided you a lesson? Explain.

_____

_____

_____

_____

_____

_____

_____

➤ What kind of lesson does each provide for you? List below.

(Example: Judgment, Doubt, Ego Activation, etc.)

_____

_____

_____

_____

_____

_____
_____
_____
_____
_____
_____
_____

2).

> **Review your post-it notes** to ensure you have worded them in a way that triggers the feeling of full pure intention. Modify the verbiage if it does not jet truth through you.

How long <u>have you complained</u> about things in your life, but when given the **opportunity to transform** them you fall back in the same old pattern that has kept you where you are?

What has **<u>prevented you</u>** from modifying your behavior?

3).

> Write down as many as you can think of, a minimum of 5.

_____
_____
_____
_____
_____
_____
_____
_____
_____
_____

- Next to each item written above, write the **emotion you feel** when you think or say it. Is it anger, frustration, sadness, doubt? Write everything you feel down. This gives us an opportunity to **"pluck" the interference!** This may take a little **soul-searching**. Award yourself the time to remove these binds that hold you back!
- **Now, write the I Am to counter-balance that which has held you back.**

4).

- **Congratulate yourself.**
- Every time you catch yourself digressing, modify behavior.
- Every time that you take an **active role in your future design**, take a moment to <u>appreciate yourself.</u>

As always, I am here for you, and I believe in you!

Day 10– Tuesday

Good Tuesday Morning!

Last Tuesday we discovered that the word Tuesday was derived from the meaning To Do Day. So today, Tuesday, let's do something about **confidence,** in particular, the lack of confidence that keeps us from believing that we have the abilities, support and information to do the things that we want to do.

This subject also ties in nicely with the below quote from, Marcus Tullius Cicero who lived from 106 BC to 43 BC. As he states, "With confidence, you have won even before you have started." That is a powerful statement of fact.

"Too often we are in a hurry to get there and miss the Journey. Slow down and see what you have been missing." Dale Lawrence

Think about something you do, or have done well. Even if that thing is something that you feel requires attention now, at some point you knew with confidence you did it well. Coloring? Riding a bike? Math? Being a student? Being a friend? Being a mom? Everyone has things that they know they did well.

Do not slip into comparing yourself to anyone else here. If I compared myself to Lance Armstrong…oops wrong example…☺, but perhaps not.

What a grand example of digging deep for confidence, learning a lesson in life, brushing yourself off, and moving forward. Imagine, being a public figure and screwing up…ouch. What confidence it would take to not only face the world again, but face you.

So your **assignment** today is counter-balancing the urge to doubt yourself, and think less of yourself than the world around you.

➢ **1).**

Stand in front of the mirror, eyes open and tell yourself the following. Repeat **seven (7) times.** When you tell these to yourself, talk to **your heart chakra**, talk to **your soul**. Look at yourself with eyes of acceptance and love, as though you are an Angel blessing yourself.

< I Believe in **You**.

< I Am Valuable.

< I Am Filled and Over-Flowing with Confidence.

< I have Everything I need to complete my Mission Statement in this life.

< I Am Happy and Laughing every day.

< I Love Me.

< I Am Very, Very Proud of Me.

< I support Me Completely and Lovingly.

< I Freely and Easily have Released All Doubt in and of me.

➢ **2).**

Say 3 to 5 more of your choosing. Write them below.

_____

_____

_____

_____

_____

_____

_____

➢ **3).**

Write down which of the above were <u>most difficult</u> for you to say and believe when you said them to yourself.

_____

_____

_____

_____

_____

_____

_____

_____

> **4).**

Write, **I Am's** on post-it notes from #1 and #2 above. Place the notes in your immediate space. Computer screen, mirror, table, refrigerator- anywhere and everywhere that will supply you a constant reminder of filling yourself with assurance of your truth's. Assuring you that you do, in fact, have all the confidence you need to live in joy, to fulfill your assignments and be the light soul you were born to be.

When you feel the pangs of emotions that limit you sneak in, grab them and pluck them from your space.

It is **Not Your Reality** to suffer with things that are not in line with the Divine Brilliance of your Soul. Remember, you have a Divine stamp of approval!

Day 11– Wednesday

Good Wednesday Morning!

"Reach out today in directions that you have not before. You never know whose hand you will find and whose soul you will help." Marilyn Lawrence

How are you doing?

Are you **grounding yourself regularly**?

Are you beginning to notice that you are **automatically correcting** yourself when you say, do or think something that you don't want back?

Are you keeping your **head in the game**?

Are you **helping others** around you when they need it? *One of Today's assignments involves reaching out to someone who needs your help.

I love the quote shared from, <u>Harrison Ford</u> in which he said, basically, to **stick with it;** many fail just because they do not. I witnessed that over and over in my past careers. People got in to the line of work because they thought it would be easy and quick money. Just to find out it was not, and gave up. All the excitement, energy and enthusiasm they once had, <u>flushed down the drain</u> with disappointment in circumstances, investment and themselves.

Some did not quit though, some struggled through the **start-up phase**, and though they watched others around them slowly drop off, and they kept their head down and did the work. Guess what happened? They won. They succeeded. They were the **<u>victors in the battle of wills</u>**.

With anything new, a workout routine, dieting, a new job, there is generally a struggle with self. Whether the struggle is with change, time restrictions…the excuses can be many, but it is **the desire** that needs the attention…to be nourished so as to continue the push forward. The initial desire that compelled you to take the first step. In your case, the list that you created that outline the life you want to live.

So **let's pump up your desire today** so that you can continue your commitment to self and goals, shall we?

Assignments:

> **1).** Sit at your table, or desk. Close your eyes. Feet flat on the floor. Imagine in your mind the life you want to live. Who is with you? What are you doing? What are your surroundings? What is the temperature? How does it feel? How does it smell? Immerse yourself completely in your experiences. Each one. Each item that you are working to manifest in your life. You should find yourself smiling, happy and in joy.
> Open your eyes and write down your full experience. Write down your feelings, your thoughts, your excitement…write down everything.

How strong is your Desire to have the things you want? Your desire should be unlimited. 100%. Fully and completely radiating through you.

If obstacles come up that try to side-track you or deflate your progression, pluck them. They are not part of your reality!

No excuses…. you do have time for <u>you</u> if this is what you **really want in your life**. **Gift yourself the time to be**.

This is only 28 days out of the rest of your life. Make it count!

Write a post-it note and write on your goal board: "I Am filled with desire to achieve those things that bring me joy and that are aligned with my greatest and highest good. There is no obstacle larger than my desire!" Wallpaper!

> **2).** Lend a **helping hand** to someone you run in to today. **Unconditionally** support another with no expectations of reciprocation.

> **3).** Wave your arms in the air and laugh freely as you do it! Yes, I am serious! Liberating!

"There is beauty all around you because there is beauty inside of you. Enjoy it! Magnify it!"

"Create as many perfect days in your life as you can by remembering that we get by giving… If we give enough we become gifted.

Give your time to those who wish they had more of it.

Give your attention to those who need and want it.

Give yourself the gift of a giving heart." Dale Lawrence

Day 12– Thursday

Good Morning and Happy Thursday!

"Dreams are a reality just waiting for the right words and actions. Always believe this, and practice it as often as you can." Marilyn Lawrence

How did yesterday's assignment with Desire go? Are you feeling more desir-ess?

Reminding oneself of the inner burnings of desire is a valuable component to fuel the drive toward a goal. Desire, like passion, feed the soul's fire.

Just like a steam engine requires coal or wood to operate and most automobiles require gasoline, the soul...our Soul, requires fuel too. What we nourish our soul with affects its performance.

Do you nourish and nurture your soul with love, compassion, understanding, and passionate desire towards purpose? Or are you feeding it with thoughts, actions, and words that have a depleting effect, literally draining the life out of your soul with unconscious behavior?

Today we will focus on the **fuel you are giving your soul**.

"Grow from your sorrows and know that wounds do

heal given time and the right medicine.

And, know that the key is within your own heart.

Start by forgiving others." Dale Lawrence

Assignments:

1). Keep your workbook close by today. You will be **journaling your pattern of soul-fuel**. Be conscious of the words that **ignite the fire** in your soul. Positively-charged words like excitement, joy, desire, passion, compassion expand the soul and its light with Divine love.

In comparison, words like judgment, envy, scorn, frustration, worthlessness, and the like are heavy and **weigh down** the energy and soul-light, basically extinguishing the light.

Throughout the day, record your pattern below. The more awareness you give to this project, the more beneficial it will be for you. Recognizing a pattern <u>awards one the opportunity</u> to refine it, to **sculpt the standard you Desire.**

2).

➤ If you find some words that are extinguishing your soul's light instead of fueling it, right the correction next to it above. Example. "That, Sally, she always requires all the attention." "Sally has a lot to offer."

3).

➤ Chant your **"I Am's"** when you go to bed. Be disciplined, every time your mind wanders, bring it back to your I Am's. You may have to do this retrieval back to center several times. That is okay. **Doing, is the way things get done.**

4).

➤ Do at least one (1) thing today to **show yourself appreciation** for making it this far in the 28 Day Sculpting. Award yourself private time, a bath, a walk. Go out for a meal. Watch a movie. Dedicate an award to your hard work. Write down how you are showing yourself appreciation.

Oops…. did a thought like, "I haven't worked that hard at this, I don't deserve to award myself," or etc. come in? You have now been gifted an awareness of two (2) things.

 1-That you know you **can do more**, and in doing so, you will feel **stronger and happier**.

 2-Recognizing this fact is more than you had before.

Award yourself anyway!

We are here to help! Thank you to those who have reached out asking for it.

Your Desire and Passion to achieve is **fueling your triumph**!

"Reduce the charge of situations you want to release or change. Given no attention, they will

no longer be part of your reality." Marilyn Lawrence

Day 13– Friday

Happy Friday,

Frid-Ah? Are you feeling fried? Do Not forget to utilize the **valuable tools of grounding and seven breaths**. (If I have not taught these to you yet, please email me and I will). These simple techniques help de-clutter and ground and work wonders and quieting the chaos around you in your mind's eye vibrational state.

You are half way in your 28 Day Sculpting. Have you been helping yourself? Have you embraced all possibilities? Have you only put one toe in, or are you fully immersed? Do you believe in yourself? **Today is good day to start if not.**

The last two days we have worked Desire, passion and the **fuel that you are feeding your soul**. How did that go? How does it feel to be conscious of the fuel that you are feeding your soul? Just as the food we feed our body effects its performance, so too does the **food we feed our mind and soul**.

Today we will continue monitoring, via journaling, the fuel you are using. We will add the second element of your triangle to trifullness; the mind. **The mind and soul**, though different, are feed with the same thoughts, actions and words.

Assignments:

1). Write down everything that makes you take pause today. Whether it is something you said, thought or did, or it was something <u>**someone else**</u> **did**. The only reason we react to some things around us and not others, is because it is touching a nerve/energy in us. A pocket of that same energy, a memory from the past or past life. This awards us a perfect time to release the vibration completely.

We may have had a past life(s) where we were shocked by the actions of those around us. That shock wave was so deep that the vibration **scarred or damaged the soul**. Until healed- released, we will continue reacting to the same things.

Writing down both internal and external triggers will award us the opportunity to make the needed adjustments…to disengage some unwanted prompts.

➢ **2).** Using Pure Intentions, **release the "gunk "that** you become aware of, or that which you are already aware of but no longer want part of your reality." It Is Not My Reality to carry that energy…work in that energy…hurt from that energy…., etc."

➢ **3). Fill yourself full and over-flowing** with <u>**Your Own**</u> Divinely washed Divinely blessed energy. Just make that statement and feel the Divine light flowing into your crown chakra energy center located at the top of your head. Feel as it runs down your back, down your throat, shoulders, arms and chest; through your heart and abdomen; down your legs. Feel Your Divinely washed Divinely blessed energy run all through you, cleansing you, loving you, healing you. Imagine if you cannot feel. Know that you know that you know you are now full and overflowing with the best of you.

How does this feel? Write it down. And, do it often!

_____

_____

_____

_____

_____

_____

_____

_____

_____

_____

_____

> **4). Notice a minimum of four (4) things** today in your environment that you had not taken time to notice before. Write them below. Show appreciation.

_____

_____

_____

_____

_____

_____

_____

_____

_____

_____

_____

I am here for you. I Believe in you. You are wearing your **Divine stamp of approval** on your forehead. NEVER forget that! **Put back your shoulders and take in the importance of that!**

"A reach without a stretch is simply a yawn. You may need to stretch for your goals." Dale Lawrence

Day 14– Saturday

Good Happy Saturday!

There are cliffs and plateaus in life; you are either climbing or resting. It is those that do not rest too long that

make it to the top. They breathe in the brilliance and truly soar." Marilyn Lawrence

Last Friday, Day we concentrated on **loving ourselves**. What could be better than to love our selves…our souls, deeply and purely? Love filled with forgiveness, enjoyment, marvel, support, gratitude and ambition? For that in fact is our reality. We are simply on different levels of appreciation to such.

Last Saturday we followed up the **pure love of "self" application** from Friday with exercises that **dedicated** our full intentions to the **design of our life**. To appreciate our individual design and support it with dedication.

Appreciation is the name of the game today. Showing/giving appreciation not only feels good, but attracts appreciation to you. We are going to combine Love and Dedication too.

"Welcome to the next first day of your Incredible Journey."

Dale Lawrence

Assignments:

1).

- This is a **two-part** assignment.
- *Know and Show* <u>**Appreciation, Love, and Dedication**</u> a minimum of <u>fifteen, (15) times</u> divided in these categories-
- Minimum Five, (5) things in your **Environment.**
- Minimum Five, (5) things about your **Life.**
- Minimum Five, (5) things about your **Self.**
- **Write these fifteen, (15) things down, and** more if you want to.

a).

- Stand in front of your mirror, eyes open looking Lovingly at yourself. **Tell yourself** the fifteen, (15) things you listed that you appreciate, love and are dedicated to.

➢ **Repeat** each three (3) times.

Example for Environment: "I appreciate and love my home and I am dedicated to having it filled with joy and family."

Example for Life: "I appreciate and love all the lessons that I have been given in life, and I am dedicated to using them to move forward."

Example of Self: "I appreciate and love that I have not given up, and I am dedicated to continuing to attract to me all my life deserves.

b).

➢ A minimum of fifteen (15) times, **show appreciation, love, and dedication to others**. Make a phone call, help someone with their groceries, show someone how to belly laugh. You will be awarded opportunities today. **Make a difference in someone else's life**. List your 15 kind acts below.

2).

➢ **Release, "pluck" any resistance** to the above if it sneaks in when performing the above. List the "plucks" below.

_____

_____

_____

_____

_____

_____

_____

_____

_____

_____

_____

_____

_____

3).

➢ **Enjoy Thoroughly the beauty of the day!**

I am here for you!

"Pay attention that every moment you are living is in
the **Now**, and that the <u>Now</u> you are living in

is taking you to where you want to be!" Marilyn Lawrence

Day 15– Sunday

Happy Sun Day!

Today marks the sixteenth day we have worked together on the **campaign designed to sculpt the desired magnificence of your life.**

By utilizing <u>simple techniques</u>, we have begun the shifting of the energy that you attract back to you, thus, **employing energy magnetism for your creation**.

You have not only taken a participatory role in your reality, but you are at the **helm** of your ship. You have the steering wheel. You know now that by making <u>simple shifts</u> in your life it will, in fact, be sailing, (or flying) in the direction <u>you</u> choose. No longer **<u>running ashore because of other's visions of you</u>**.

We ARE Proud of You! Be Proud of Yourself Too! This truly is Brilliant!

We are in the **last two weeks** of your energy sculpting…twelve, (12) days left. Your daily assignments will modify to three, (3) times a week for the last two weeks. Day 18-Tuesday, Day 20- Thursday, Day 23- Sunday, Day 25- Tuesday and Day 28- Friday.

This time is for you. These assignments are for you. The love that is shared through each word is for you. Might I suggest you put your gears in over-drive to make the most of our time together? Why not? What are 12 more days out of the rest of your life? Try it. Do it. Embrace it. Over-drive it!

As you may have assumed already, since you will be receiving just three, (3) emails a week, the assignments on each of these days will larger to be performed over the time between. Let's kick the assignment results out of the park, shall we?

You should by now be consciously **grounding every day**, throughout the day. This is as common-place a daily procedure as brushing your teeth.

Assignments:

> **1). Y**our home and/or work space should look like **"confetti" of post-it notes**. What a **brilliant way to show the universe** that you are <u>serious</u> about the life you are sculpting!

Have you **added post-it's** as things have come up? Continue to do this, forever.

The simple act of committing to paper that which you want to attract, gives **permanence to your reality.**

>**Review all your post-it notes**. Write each one below. As you read each one, <u>**note your reaction**</u> to it. Did it make you happy, warm, stressed?

Send me the ones that are still difficult/challenging for you to read/hear, imagine and accept. We will **work together** on them.

➤ **2). Review your goal board**. Write each goal below. As you read each one, **note your reaction** to it. Did it make you happy, warm, stressed?

Send me the ones that are difficult for you. We will **work together** on the ones that are still challenging for you to read/hear, imagine and accept.

➤ **3).** Think outside the box. **Think bigger,** do not limit yourself. Remember, God and his Angels hold your road map of past, present, and future. Do not think small. You will attract to you what is in line with your highest and greatest good as it relates to your life's mission statement. **Ignite the energy of Abundance.**

> Write **seven, (7)** additional Post-it note I Am's based on the **principle of Abundance.** List them above too.

Example: "I Am Abundance of all that I need in my life."

➤ **4). Chant.** Every night for the balance of the 28 days. Better yet, continue for the rest of your life.

➤ **5). Monitor your "Balance" throughout the day.**

Morning- How do you feel when you **first get up**? Record it.

_____
_____

12:00- How do you feel at mid-day? Record it.

_____
_____

3:00- How do you feel in late afternoon? Record it.

_____
_____

7:00- How do you feel in the evening? Record it.

_____
_____

The goal is to have equal balance throughout the day so that you can **apply balanced energy to progression.** Determining our most effective and least effective times during the day supplies needed information that is two-pronged. First, it gives us an opportunity to supply energy to the times that need it, building the energy effectiveness. Second, it allows us **immediate opportunities** to tap into the highest times of your day. To be completely aware of your energy swings for optimized efficiency.

> ➤ **6). Judgment**. How many times during the day are you **judging yourself?** Write down every time you do.

Make the most of this time together!

Beautiful things are happening. With knowledge and awareness things blossom. Be sure to nourish yourself as you blossom!

"The distance between winning and losing is the

length of your own belief system."

Dale Lawrence

Day 17– Tuesday

Good Beauty-full morning!

So, how did you do with this last Sunday's assignments?
Adding post-it notes to your (hopefully) already wallpapered space?

Reviewing your post-it notes and goal board?

Thinking bigger. ..Bringing in Abundance? "This or something better" philosophy?

Chanting?

Balance during the day, determining when your highest balance is, and when you are least balanced?

Judgment?

"Live in the Present.

Live in the Now.

What are you <u>thinking</u> this very moment?

Is it something that will make you better or

make you worse?

Is it something that will move you toward your dream, or
hold you in place, or even worse, move you

away from your dream?" Marilyn Lawrence

That is quite an assignment list! Mastering anyone of those would create
A large shift!
There are a couple I wish to concentrate on further, actually three because of the importance.

<u>Assignments:</u>

So your assignments today and for the next couple days are directly aligned with Sunday's, taking them to probing depths for understanding:

> **1).** <u>Balance</u>.

a). If you have not written down the times of the day that you feel the <u>most</u> balanced and the <u>least</u> balanced, do so for the next 5 days. Look for a pattern to emerge.

b). List the triggers that relate to the shifts in balance. Example: Is there a co-worker/spouse/family member that triggers lack of balance and thus, energy? Perhaps one that triggers higher balance, thus, energy? Is the shift food amplified? Be attentive to detail.

> **2). Abundance.** Practice the mindset of-"this or something better." No more limiting you! When you look at your goals and post it notes, have thoughts in your head that are always open to unlimited possibilities. Don't ask for one when the Angels were going to give you two. Example: "I would like to retire in 5 years, or sooner." "I would like to go on a two-week vacation or longer."

Write a minimum of 5 limitless thinking mantras below.

> **3). Judgment.** For the next 5 days' write down every time you passed judgment either on yourself or on someone else.

Next to each occurrence write how it made you feel. "Good because they deserved it...it is true,", "badly because. ..." . Be Consciously aware of this. Write it down.

_____

_____

_____

_____

_____

_____

_____

_____

_____

_____

_____

_____

_____

_____

_____

_____

_____

I am available to you when you need me! Simply email me with thoughts and concerns.
Sending you all pure love on this ridiculously amazing day!

"Successful people always make the last step of a journey the
first step of new one." Dale Lawrence

Day 19– Thursday

"If you <u>Believe</u> it, Then it is.

If you <u>Think</u> it, then it is.

If you <u>Dream</u> it, then it is.

If you think it can not be, then it is."

Marilyn Lawrence

Good Thursday Morning!

Since much of our daily action is supported by more than just our thinking, words, and actions but also include strong abilities that everyone has hidden from the immediate sight, we will focus on these the next few days. Increasing awareness, recognizing the constant aid they lend us and incorporating them into our daily routine to heighten our results.

The abilities to which I am referring are what I fondly refer to as our, "Claire's."
Clairsentience: You Feel things.
If your primary psychic modality is clairsentience, which means clear-feeling, begin paying attention to a tug or feeling in your midsection. Or you might feel a hot or cold sensation. You might feel a tingling sensation in your hands. Don't use your logic. Turn down your analyzer gage. Feel for the tugging, temperature, or tingle.

Use Clairvoyance: You See Things.
If your primary psychic modality is clairvoyance, which means clear-seeing, sit quietly, get meditative, and ask your question. Then allow an image to form in your mind's eye. Maybe you'll see a movie play out in your mind. Maybe you'll just see a picture. Maybe you'll get a symbol or metaphor that must be figured out.

Use Clairaudience: You Hear Things.
If your primary psychic modality is clairaudience, which means clear-hearing, sit quietly, get meditative, and call in your mind whatever question you have. Listen for the answer. Again, you're going to have to push your logic away. Remember, just because a message comes in your voice, does not mean it is not a message for you.

Use Claircognizance: You Know.
If your primary psychic modality is claircognizance, which means clear-knowing, then turn off your rational mind completely and simply know, with confidence and assurance. Don't even think about it, just trust and know. Yep, this one's hard if you're not a gifted claircognizant.

"We are All Searching for the 'Perfect' That We came from.

The *perfect* that will last longer than a moment or two in time.

The perfection of Oneness, Wholeness, and Bliss.

It is that which makes the quest so difficult." Marilyn Lawrence

To be able to think and act beyond the immediate visible, and trust without doubting is vitally important to allowing all the external and internal help you are not only deserving of, but require for ultimate progression. Many people have an almost immediate doubt trigger which flares when they hear talk of a third eye, or being physic. The truth is we were all gifted with many abilities that sadly, have been closed down and repressed over time. Conformity of thinking and acting has been promoted, instead of divergent creation.

So your assignments this week will be working with these invisible energy fields, calling in your awareness of them, promoting the allowance of use and embracing without doubt the importance of living in the full gifts of you.

Assignments:

➤ **1).** Read through the 4 categories of Claire's above- Clairsentience, Clairaudience, Clairaudience, Claircognizance. Which are you initially drawn to, identify with? Which did you immediately recognize as one of your abilities that you have used before? Perhaps you were unaware of it before now. List below and your recall of usage.

We will work with the first two on the above list for the next 3 days. Feeling and Seeing. Engaging your invisible energy field to feel more. In doing so, you will have a better awareness of what is around you. What is not serving you well and requires "cleaning."

Clairsentience: You Feel things.

If your primary psychic modality is clairsentience, which means clear-feeling, begin paying attention to a tug or feeling in your midsection. Or you might feel a hot or cold sensation. You might feel a tingling sensation in your hands. Don't use your logic. Turn down your analyzer gage. Feel for the tugging, temperature, or tingle.

> **1).** Devote time over the next three days to feeling your environment at work, at home, in your travels, everywhere the next three days take you. Record how each feels to you. When someone enters your space, how does it feel? When an incidence happens, how does it feel? Recognize when your clairsentience is warning you of energy that is not good for you or of situations where the energy is not in alignment with where you want to be in your life.

Record every action and reaction below. Use the back if necessary. Becoming aware of the unseen energy vibrations so that you can monitor and adjust them is essential to easier forward progression.

_____

_____

_____

_____

_____

_____

Use Clairvoyance: You See Things.

If your primary psychic modality is clairvoyance, which means clear-seeing, sit quietly, get meditative, and ask your question. Then allow an image to form in your mind's eye. Maybe you'll see a movie play out in your mind. Maybe you'll just see a picture. Maybe you'll get a symbol or metaphor that must be figured out.

> ➤ **2).** Devote time over the next three days to seeing in your mind's eye triggers in your environment at work, at home, in your travels, everywhere the next three days take you. Record what you see and are shown. When someone enters your space, what do you see? When an incidence happens, what do you see? Recognize when your clairvoyance is warning you of energy that is not good for you or of situations where the energy is not in alignment with where you want to be in your life. Do not push this or be concerned if you are unable to "see" immediately. Just like anything else, using abilities that you have not used in some time, or perhaps never to your knowledge takes time. We are opening up to these abilities and asking that you be given/reminded of the application.

Record every action and reaction below. Use the back if necessary. Becoming aware of the unseen energy vibrations so that you can monitor and adjust them is essential to easier forward progression.

_____

_____

_____

_____

_____

_____

_____

_____

_____

_____

_____

_____

_____

_____

_____

_____

_____

_____

_____

_____

_____

_____

_____

_____

➢ **3).** With recognition comes adjustment. In both of the exercises above you listed positive and less-than-positive experiences. Addressing just the less-than-positive experiences.

Write recognitions and I Am counters next to each.

Design "I Am's" on post-it notes to create counterbalance. Place them in the space that requires adjustment.

Recognition examples: "I noticed when I was around; so-in-so I didn't feel great." Or "I noticed that the room I am in feels heavy." Or, "When I allowed myself to be in a meditative state, I could "see" the heaviness around a person and how their energy did not align with mine."

I Am examples: "I Am increasingly aware of my environment and its effects on me." "I Am creating shields to protect me against things that block my positive energy flow." "I Am no longer affected by the feelings of_____."

"Preparation is the thing that will define our future." Dale Lawrence

Day 22– Sunday

<u>Happy Sunday Morning!</u>

On Thursday we started work on developing your Claire's. How did it go? Some of the Claire's will be easier for you than other's depending on what your strong natural abilities are. Others may take longer to develop. Continued attention and usage will aid you in many ways in life. As it is known, we utilize a minute amount of our brains abilities. The same is true with other talents that we have been gifted. Increasing awareness, developing senses, taking control of energies are our chose and right.

"By creating a better awareness for yourself,

you are awarding others by example,

the opportunity to create their own better self and

awaken their gifted life purpose." Marilyn Lawrence

For the next two days you will work on the last of the two Claire's, **Clairaudience and Claircognizance**. Again, do not push. Do not over think or have unrealistic expectations. Begin working these gifts, continue working these gifts, and allow them to help you the way they are intended to.

Use Clairaudience: You Hear Things.
If your primary psychic modality is clairaudience, which means clear-hearing, sit quietly, get meditative, and call in your mind whatever question you have. Listen for the answer. Again, you're going to have to push your logic away. Remember, just because a message comes in your voice, does not mean it is not a message for you.

> **1).** Devote time over the next two days to hearing in your environment at work, at home, in your travels, everywhere the next three days take you. Record what you hear- the messages that come to you. Remember, just because a message is in your own voice, does not mean that it is not a sent message for you. If you ask, you will receive. Have Faith that you are receiving what you need. Pay attention, receive and then apply.

Record every action and reaction below. Use the back if necessary. Becoming aware of the messages sent to you, and the realization that you are receiving them is huge! Just allow.

Use Claircognizance: You Know.

If your primary psychic modality is Claircognizance, which means clear-knowing, then turn off your rational mind completely and simply know, with confidence and assurance. Don't even think about it, just trust and know. Yep, this one's hard if you're not a gifted claircognizant.

> **2).** Devote time over the next two days to knowing that you know that you know. What knowingness is triggered in your environment at work, at home, in your travels, everywhere the next two days take you? Record what your experiences. When someone enters your space, what do you know? When an incidence happens, what do you know? Recognize when your Claircognizance is warning you of energy that is not good for you or of situations where the energy is not in alignment with where you want to be in your life. Do not push this. Just like anything else, applying abilities that you have not used in some time, or perhaps never to your knowledge, takes time. We are opening up to these abilities and asking that you be given/reminded of the application.

Record every action and reaction below. Use the back if necessary. Becoming aware of the gifts that you possess, and the unseen energy vibrations so that you can monitor and adjust them, are essential to easier forward progression.

_____

_____

_____

_____

_____

_____

_____

_____

_____

_____

_____

_____

_____

➤ **3).** With recognition comes adjustment. In both of the exercises above you listed positive and less-than-positive experiences. Addressing just the less-than-positive experiences.

Write recognitions and I Am counters next to each.

Design "I Am's" on post-it notes to create counterbalance. Place them in the space that requires adjustment.

Recognition examples: "I noticed when I was around; so-in-so I didn't feel great." Or "I noticed that the room I am in feels heavy." Or, "When I allowed myself to be in a meditative state, I could "see" the heaviness around a person and how their energy did not align with mine."

I Am examples: "I Am increasingly aware of my environment and its effects on me." "I Am creating shields to protect me against things that block my positive energy flow." "I Am no longer affected by the feelings of_____."

"Change through 'Need' is short-lived. Change through Desire and Implementation is life-long." Dale Lawrence

Day 24– Tuesday

Happy Tuesday Morning!

This is the second to last assignment you will receive with your life sculpting via energy magnetism.

> "Stay neutral to your Fear trigger.
>
> Stay neutral to all the negative triggers.
>
> Neutral attracts nothing but Neutral." Marilyn Lawrence

On Sunday your assignments included work on judgment. I received a beautiful email where the person described an "ah-ha" moment when contemplating the full impacts of both judging and being judged. Realizing that one prompted the other is really staggering. "When you judge, so shall you be judged."

What was your reaction to judgment?

This will be an ongoing correction for some, because since the day we were born we have heard judgment around us. We were taught to judge. Let me clarify something, having discernment and an opinion is not judging, but having an opinion that judges is...does that make sense?

Your second assignment Sunday was **Abundance**. Another difficult one for a number of reasons. One being, many of us were told we couldn't afford it." What a wonderful thing it would be if parents instead taught their children the law of attraction? "The universe provides to us all we need if it is aligned with our greatest and highest good. So let's send a message to the universe that we want it, and then let's actively participate how it will happen." Just thinking on paper...

It is **Awareness** that should be utilized with each of the energies created with words, actions and thoughts that we are shifting.

Today's assignments are based on **developing and capitalizing** on this awareness.

Remember, your 28-day challenge is almost over. Let's put this into over-drive!

Assignments:

> **1).** Keep this workbook and pen with you today and tally the number of times that you limit yourself with lack of abundance thinking. Example: "Oh I could never do that" …. I could never get that promotion". I can't afford it" and etc.

Write down, below what you say that is lack of abundance, and defeating/deflating.

Correct the thinking/words/actions as many times as you can. Example: oops…" I mean I have abundance of all that is good in my life and what I want and need is always supplied to me."

➢ **2).** Tally the number of times that you passed judgment. Write down any common threads. Like you judge people for particular actions, looks, and etc. Correct the thinking. Example: "Forgive me for passing judgment."

➤ **3).** Tally the number of times you felt judged. Write down what each of the situations that made you feel judged was. Read back through each. Do you see a common thread?

Example: Some people might be sensitive to the inflections in someone's voice when they are spoken to. Some people may be sensitive to the way someone looks at them. Others may think they are being told what to do all the time. These may go way back to childhood…. even past life situations. Once a common thread is identified, u takes it easier to release that which no longer serves you and is getting in the way o you forward progression.

If you are having difficulty, then email me!

_____

_____

_____

_____

_____

_____

_____

_____

_____

_____

_____

_____

_____

As always, we are here for you and support the magnificence of you! It truly is spectacular!

"A Scent in the air, the tear on our cheek, and the

laughter around us...

These are all pieces of life that we sometimes take for granted."

Dale Lawrence

Day 28– Saturday
the fin*ally

Good morning and welcome to the last day of this 28 Day Sculpting Your Life Challenge.

Congratulations on your dedication to self…to you, and to the life you know you deserve!

How did you do? Better than you initially thought you would?

Not as well as you hoped?

The wonderful thing about life is it provides do-over's!

For those that are dedicated enough to <u>live their desired dreams</u>, the end of a challenge can simply mean <u>the beginning</u>. The beginning of digging deeper for commitment, finding strength you had not discovered before…or had forgotten about, and proving to yourself that you can do it!

What a marvel!

This, our last day together, is a focus on the last 28 Days coupled with your visions of the future.

Do you still feel the excitement when you think of the things you wrote on your goal board and post-it notes?

Do you feel deflated?

Do you feel encouraged?

How about *ridiculously excited* about unlimited possibilities?

All are good, because they create your gage.

Assignments:

> **1).** Today I want you to write a recap, as long as you want, of the last 28 days. Be honest with yourself. Use additional paper if needed.

What was easy?

What was hard?

What worked best?

Why didn't you participate?

What brought you the most joy? And, etc.

➢ **2).** Congratulate yourself for everything good you did over the last 28 days. Everything!

No focusing on what was not done. <u>Only</u> what <u>was</u> done. Be enthusiastic about your "goods" and allow this enthusiasm to carry you throughout the day, inspiring you to do more. Write a minimum of 5 congratulations to yourself below.

_____

_____

_____

_____

_____

_____

_____

_____

_____

➢ **3).** Go back through your 28 day workbook and work on as much as you want to. Knowing that anything you do to trigger the life you want is as easy as shifting the energy flow.

➢ **4).** Look at your Life/Vision board. What do you want to add? What do you want to change? Modify it to today's energy and progressive thinking!!!

Continue Monitoring. Continue Shifting when things don't feel right. You have awareness now. Do not put this awareness to the side and go back to old patterns. Instead, nourish the awareness with attention and action.

It is a beautiful award when you to take the labor of planting a seed, and then watch it grow before your eyes, reaching high for the light, wilting when not watered, thriving when praised.

Of course if you feel you need more hands on help you can sign up for the next Master 28, and then again and again, until the wants you have are the realities you have.

We are here to help. It is our pleasure!

With pure love we wish you a beautiful Day 28!

<u>Frequent Stumbles:</u>

"Pay Attention to the fact that you do have all the

information needed for your life.

You are simply

awakening what you know."

Marilyn Lawrence

"Embrace the word, 'Integrity.'
It is a word with many meanings that all start with ourselves, what we
do and how we interact with the world." Dale Lawrence

"Pay Attention to the fact that not everyone is learning the
same lessons in this life, and not everyone has the
same path to their purpose.
Show Respect!"

Marilyn Lawrence

"The future is yours. It belongs to you.

It is your undiscovered life.

Embrace it, take control of it and inspire yourself!" Dale Lawrence

"Pay Attention to not put limits on you. You do have the ability to manifest greatness beyond your wildest imagination.

You have sent the messages out to the universe.

Allow it to unfold the way it needs to, aligned with your highest and greatest good.
Do not under estimate, or put restraints on your outcome.

Do not expect a pebble when you could have mountains.

It is all yours. Your dreams are waiting.
There is nothing, and no one stopping you.
Start"
Marilyn Lawrence

"Live <u>YOUR LIFE</u> Out Loud and On Purpose!" Dale Lawrence

73539601R00080

Made in the USA
San Bernardino, CA
07 April 2018